Little White Cabin

Story / Illustration
by
Ferguson Plain

dedicated to...
my old friend Danny

1992

Sometimes as I walked through the bush, I would pass ol' Danny's house.
Danny was an elder who lived in a little white cabin in the bush.

One day I came upon the little white cabin and there was ol' Danny sitting on his porch, staring into the distance.

A couple of weeks later as I was walking through the bush, I came upon the little white cabin and there was ol' Danny sitting on his porch. This time I decided to say something to him.

"Aniish naa." I shouted.
Danny looked over at me. Then he stood up and slowly walked into his house without even a wave or a smile.

From that day on, every time I passed the little white cabin in the bush, there would be ol' Danny sitting on his porch, staring into the distance. And every time I saw Danny I would shout, "Aniish naa."

Then Danny would stand up and slowly walk into his house without even a wave or a smile. This happened every time I saw Danny sitting on his porch.

Until one day I was walking through the bush, as I always did I came upon the little white cabin and there was ol' Danny sitting on his porch, staring into the distance and like always I shouted to Danny, "Aniish naa."

I expected ol' Danny to stand up and walk slowly into his house without even a wave or a smile, like always. But not this time, Danny looked over at me and with a pleasant shout he answered, "Giiuk."

I stood there in the bush with the biggest smile ever. From then on when I went for walks in the bush and came upon the little white cabin, there would be ol' Danny sitting on his porch, staring into the distance and I would shout, "Aniish naa", and ol' Danny would look over to me and with a pleasant shout answer, "Giiuk."

One day my auntie made some Nboop. My auntie makes really good Nboop, the best around. I asked Auntie if she could spare some Nboop. I told her that I would like to take some to the elder who lived in the little white cabin in the bush.

"A-How," Auntie replied. She filled up a pot and gave it to me to give to the elder in the little white cabin.

I started my journey through the bush with a pot of Nboop. As I was walking, I could smell the Nboop. The smell was making me hungry.

*W*hen I finally arrived at the little white cabin in the bush, there was ol' Danny sitting on his porch, staring into the distance. I approached Danny with my pot of Nboop. This time Danny spoke first.

"*Boozhoo. Aniish naa.*"

"*Giiuk,*" I answered.

"*Aniish ezhnikaazyin?*" Danny asked.

"*Waaboozoons n'dizhnikaaz.*" "I'm from the far side of the reserve".

"What's in the pot, *Waaboozoons?*" Danny asked.

"I brought some Nboop for you. *Kii wiisin naa?*" "*Kaa.*" Danny replied.

"*Maanda.* This is for you."

Danny took the pot from my hands and with a soft smile said, "Miigwech."

Danny then stood up and went into the house. He looked back and invited me in, "Biindigen,"

"A-How," I said.

From then on, I often visited Danny, who lived in the little white cabin in the bush. Sometimes we would sit for hours while Danny, sipping his niibiishaaboo, told his legends and talked of many, many things.

As the months passed Danny and I grew closer and closer. On some occasions I felt his spirit touch mine.

Whenever Danny and I went for walks in the bush, he showed me many plants used for medicine. And he talked to me about his family and clan and I talked to him about mine.

One day Danny gave me a braid of sweetgrass. I was curious why he gave me such a gift, so I asked him, "Danny, why did you give me such a sacred gift?"

He looked at me. "This sweetgrass that I give to you will hold many prayers and visions, and this gift will give the scent of Mother Earth, for you hold many spirits within this braid of sweetgrass."

I held this gift close to my heart, knowing that this gift was special.

One day Danny and I went for a walk in the bush. It was just before dusk and ol' Danny wanted to pick mushrooms for supper. As we were walking, I heard the sound of an owl, so I looked up and Danny looked up too, and there was the biggest owl I had ever seen.

Danny said softly, "We must not scare the owl. We must honour it. They are said to hold the spirits of our elders." So we just stood there looking at it. And when the owl suddenly flew away, a look of comfort came over Danny's face, for he knew what that owl had wanted.

That night Danny cooked up all the mushrooms we had picked, and boy, were they good.

As I grew up, ol' Danny grew older, until one day as I was walking through the bush like I always did, I came upon the little white cabin. Danny wasn't sitting on his porch, staring into the distance.

As I stood there looking at the little white cabin in the bush, a gentle wind blew around me, as if it was making friends with me. Then I heard an owl in the distance, and I understood that I wouldn't see ol' Danny again.

To this day, I can still remember what ol' Danny had said to me once, while we were walking through the bush.

Little One

Little one, there will be a time when I will no longer take walks in the bush and enjoy the pleasures of Mother Earth — like the sound of a raindrop, the scent of burning sweetgrass — for I will be the wind, the moon, and the stars in the sky. So when I'm gone, it's up to you to carry on.

GLOSSARY

Giiuk - fine

Aniish naa? - how are you?

Nboop - soup

Boozhoo - hello

Aniish ezhnikaazyin? - what's your name?

Waaboozoons - little rabbit

N'dizhnikazz - my name is

Kaa - no

Maanda - here

Kii wiisin naa? - did you eat?

A-How - okay

Biindigen - come in

Miigwech - thank you

Niibiishaaboo - tea